BEASTS OF TOLKIEN

A COLOURING BOOK

An Hachette UK Company
www.hachette.co.uk

First published in 2016 by Cassell,
a division of Octopus Publishing Group Ltd
Carmelite House
50 Victoria Embankment
London, EC4Y 0DZ
www.octopusbooks.co.uk

ISBN: 978 0 75373 083 6

A CIP catalogue record for this book is available from the British Library

Printed and bound in China

10 9 8 7 6 5 4 3 2 1

Publisher: Sam Warrington
Design: Megan van Staden
Editor: Phoebe Morgan
Administrative Assistant: Sarah Vaughan
Senior Production Manager: Katherine Hockley

This book contains references to Elvish names. All efforts have been taken to ensure these are as accurate as etymologically possible, however in some cases the closest possible interpretation has been used where a clear name is not available.

ABOUT THE ARTISTS

Born and raised in Milan, **MAURO MAZZARA** started drawing at the age of two . . . and he still hasn't stopped! He attended the Arte & Messaggio Illustration school in Milan before studying painting at the Brera Art Academy. Published worldwide, he won several prizes as a painter and illustrator. He now works as a freelance illustrator for the fashion, publishing and advertising industries.

—

ANDREA PIPARO was born in Rome in 1990, where he graduated from art school in via Ripetta and continued his studies by attending the illustration course at the International School of Comics. He has appeared in various collective exhibitions, produced several portraits on commission and contributed to the 2013 calendar of the Italian National Police.

—

WELCOME TO THE WORLD OF TOLKIEN

The fantasy world of J. R. R. Tolkien is writhing with beasts: large and small, deadly and devious, weak and powerful - and they are found everywhere: on land, under the sea and in the sky. From fire-breathing dragons to the dead men of the marshes, horrors lurk around every corner - and this book showcases them all.

The intricate line art found on these pages gives you the chance to harness your creativity and delve into the depths of the darkness: colour in Balrogs and hobgoblins, Dark Elves and spiders, giants and trolls.

Tolkien's greatest creations can all be found in this book; surround yourself with Sauron, Shelob, and Gollum, all set against the magnificent backdrops of Middle-earth, the Undying Lands, and the caves of Cirith Ungol.

Bring this great author's work to life and let your imagination run free as the creatures of *The Hobbit, The Silmarillion,* and *The Lord of the Rings* do battle on every page. It's the perfect form of escapism, so open up and let the magic of Middle-earth pull you under. . .

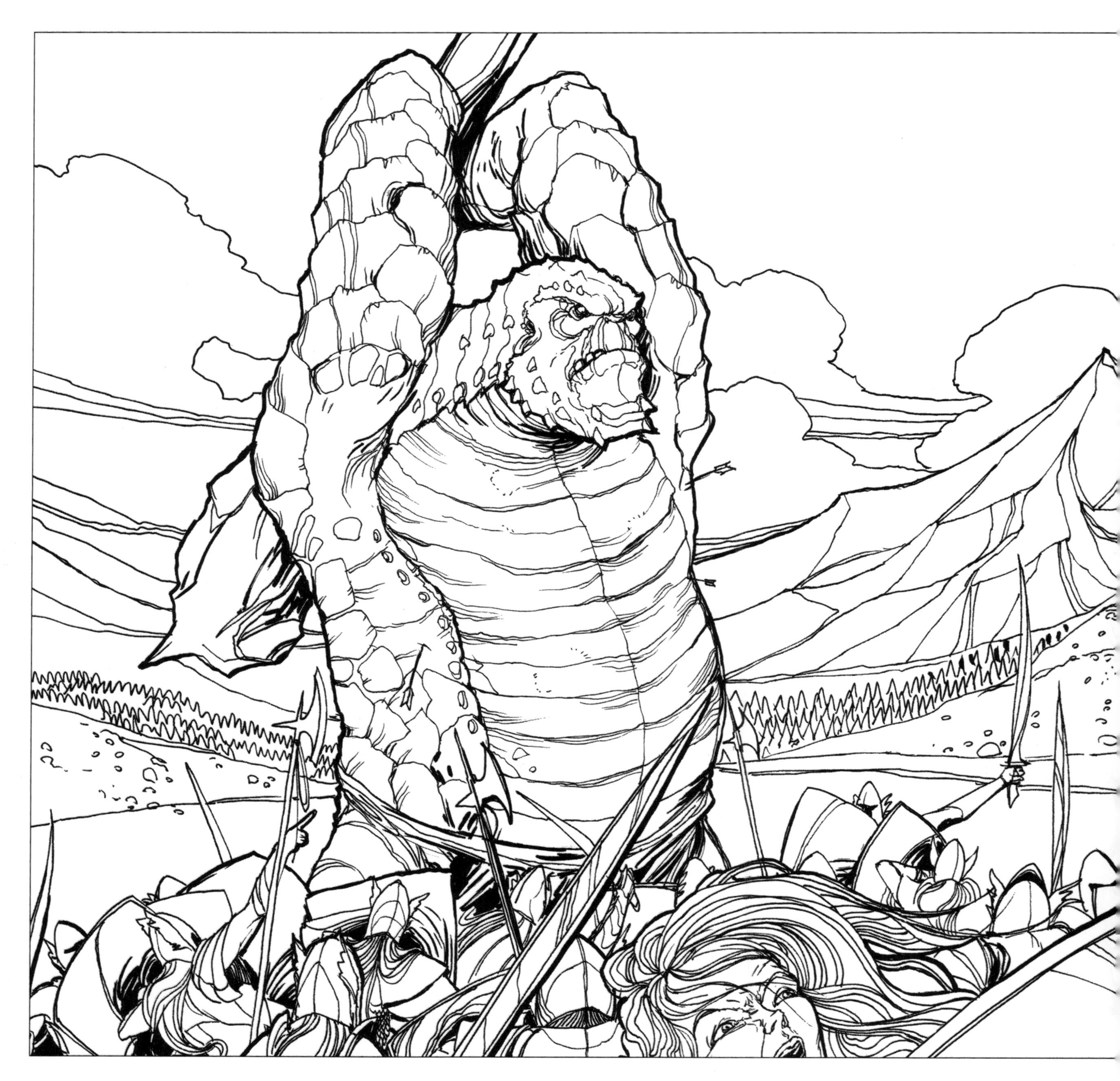